felicity Wishes®

LIQUORICE LACE ROOM

fairy fun

and other stories

Hodder
Children's
Books

A division of Hachette Children's Books

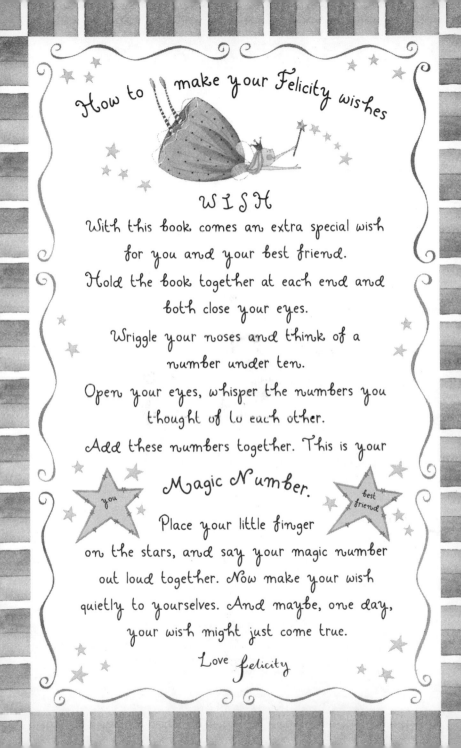

How to make your Felicity wishes

WISH

With this book comes an extra special wish for you and your best friend.

Hold the book together at each end and both close your eyes.

Wriggle your noses and think of a number under ten.

Open your eyes, whisper the numbers you thought of to each other.

Add these numbers together. This is your

Magic Number.

Place your little finger on the stars, and say your magic number out loud together. Now make your wish quietly to yourselves. And maybe, one day, your wish might just come true.

Love felicity

For Daisy Lucia Lord,
with sparkling wishes, Auntie Emma x

Emma Thomson's
felicity Wishes®

FELICITY WISHES
Felicity Wishes © 2000 Emma Thomson
Licensed by White Lion Publishing

Text and Illustrations © 2006 Emma Thomson

First published in Great Britain in 2006 by Hodder Children's Books

The right of Emma Thomson to be identified as the author and illustrator of this work has
been asserted by her in accordance with the Copyright, Designs and Patents Act 1988.

1

A Catalogue record for this book is available from the British Library

ISBN-10: 0340 917482
ISBN-13: 9780340917480

Printed and bound in Great Britain by Bookmarque Ltd, Croydon, Surrey

The paper and board used in this paperback by Hodder Children's Books are natural recyclable
products made from wood grown in sustainable forests. The manufacturing processes
conform to the environmental regulations of the country of origin.

Hodder Children's Books
A division of Hachette Children's Books, 338 Euston Road, London NW1 3BH

CONTENTS

Sensational Sweets

Fairy Fun

Circus Cheer

Sensational Sweets

Felicity Wishes and her friends Holly, Polly, Daisy and Winnie were all feeling a little down in the dumps. It didn't seem as though anything was going right. Each of them had had one sort of catastrophe or another over the last few days. But it was Polly who'd had more than her fair share...

"I've had it!" burst out Polly as she

joined her friends at break-time that morning.

"Are you still upset about losing your maths homework on the way to school?" asked Felicity.

Polly shook her head in despair.

"You're not still worried about that stain on the star of your wand?" ventured Holly. "You know, in some fairy countries it's considered lucky when a bird does that!"

Polly looked doubtfully at the end of her wand and grimaced. "Nope," she said. "That's nothing. But on the way to weightlifting class last night my bike got a puncture and by the time I'd mended it I'd missed the entire thing!"

"Oh, no!" said Felicity, hugging Polly. She knew how much weightlifting class meant to her friend. Polly wanted to be a Tooth Fairy when she graduated and it was essential that she was able to lift heavy pillows.

Polly began to sob. All this bad luck was really getting to her.

"You know," she said, imploring her friends, "I always try to do my best. I'm never naughty, I always hand my homework in on time and I keep my house neat and tidy. So why is all this bad luck happening to me?"

Felicity, Winnie, Holly and Daisy looked blankly at their friend. They didn't know what to say.

"Well," said Polly with a new determination in her voice, "if bad luck happens whether you're a conscientious fairy or not then I see little point in trying my best all the time!"

Felicity, Holly, Daisy and Winnie looked at their friend aghast.

"What are you saying?" asked Felicity, fearing the worst.

"I'm saying… I think it's time we stopped being so sensible and started having some fun!"

* * *

The five fairy friends had lost no time getting their new priorities in order. That afternoon, instead of sitting at the front of chemistry class like they usually did, they sat right at the back. They barely listened to a word Miss Sparkle said and instead thought up fantastic fun things to do!

"We could hire superspeed flying bikes for the

day," suggested Felicity, "and cycle somewhere we've never been before."

"Or we could check in for a weekend of pampering at the Fairy Spa," said Daisy.

"I know, let's go to the Sweet Factory this weekend!" proposed Polly.

Felicity couldn't believe her ears. Polly wanted to be a Tooth Fairy, so she never ever ate sweets!

Miss Sparkle couldn't believe what she was hearing either.

"FAIRIES!" she shouted. "This is no time for gossiping! I'm surprised at you. What's got into you all today? Please mix the two compounds carefully and then come to me to get it marked."

"We can't go to the Sweet Factory this weekend," said Felicity, whispering over her shoulder. "We've got the school camping trip to the Lakes."

"I'm sure they won't miss us just

this once," said Polly, feeling very naughty indeed.

The fairy friends had never seen this rebellious side of Polly and didn't know what to say.

"Sweets or a geography trip," said Polly, waving her wand in the air. "What's more fun?"

The answer was obvious.

* * *

Felicity had never felt the thrill of naughtiness quite so much. They'd all written sick notes to Fairy Godmother, excusing themselves from the school trip.

"Is everyone ready?" said Polly, hovering excitedly above her fairy friends early on Saturday morning. "Where's Daisy?"

Daisy was notoriously dreamy. One day she wanted to become a Blossom Fairy and she spent most of her time daydreaming about

becoming a world-famous gardener.

"She's probably forgotten all about going to the Sweet Factory and has gone on the geography trip," ventured Felicity.

"We can't go and get her, or Fairy Godmother will see that our excuse about being poorly isn't true!" said Holly.

Polly thought for a moment. "Then we'll have to go without her."

Felicity didn't like to leave Daisy out, but she also didn't want to miss out on such an exciting trip so, reluctantly, she flew off with the others. Felicity had always had a sweet tooth, and this trip was a dream come true.

* * *

But Daisy hadn't forgotten about going to the Sweet Factory.

Being dreamy meant she thought a lot. And what she thought was that she would spend the whole day worrying about whether they would be found out. She wasn't sure that missing the trip would be as much fun as Polly was promising.

* * *

The Sweet Factory was more mind-blowing than Felicity had ever imagined. The sugar-coated glass castle stood on a hill so high that

it could be seen from miles around.
When the sun came up behind the hill
it cast brilliantly coloured reflections of
the rainbow sweets being made inside.

When they saw its enormous golden gates, the fairies soon forgot all about the geography trip they were missing and flew inside without a second thought. The magical rainbow exterior was nothing compared to what the fairies found inside. It took their breath away. The castle was divided up into hundreds of glass rooms and leading to these glass rooms were dozens of tiny corridors. Each corridor and room was lit in a different hue of the rainbow.

As Felicity, Holly, Polly and Winnie stood in the grand reception hall they tried hard to find the source of its lilac light. Bafflingly, there wasn't a single sweet in sight.

"Four for the full guided tour," said Polly to the lilac Ticket Fairy behind the counter.

"Are you with a school party?" she

asked, looking up at Polly and her single wings. Fully fledged fairies who had graduated from school wore double wings.

Felicity shifted nervously. If the ticket fairy found out they were supposed to be on a trip with the School of Nine Wishes then Fairy Godmother would be informed instantly.

"Yes, yes, we are. We're doing a special project on the magic of sweets," replied Polly, confidently.

Felicity gasped. The Ticket Fairy looked up and gave her a hard frown. Felicity swiftly put her hand over her mouth and pretended that she had actually yawned.

"What sort of school project?" asked the Ticket Fairy suspiciously. It was obvious she didn't believe them.

"On colour!" said Holly quickly, anxious to change the subject.

"Where exactly does this lovely lilac colour come from?"

Holly's distraction technique worked more thoroughly than she'd expected. Half an hour later the fairies were still in the reception hall and none of them had their tickets!

"So you see," said the Ticket Fairy, finally drawing breath, "lilac has always been my favourite colour, and when this job was advertised in *The Daily Flutter* I knew I was made for it. Amazing though, isn't it, that the colour originates from the magic of the sweet itself. This isn't true lilac, of course, it's an overspill from the Blackcurrant Twist booth which is the first room you'll visit on your tour."

"Talking of which…" urged Holly, able to get a word in at last.

"Oh, yes," said the Ticket Fairy, reaching towards her printer, which whirred out four golden tickets. "If

you'd like to walk through
to the first room, a fairy
will join you shortly
for your guided
tour."

The Ticket Fairy had been right. The
beautiful and intense lilac colour the
fairies had experienced in the
entrance hall was nothing to the rich
lilac purple of the Blackcurrant Twist
booth. What they didn't expect,
though, was to be hit full-on with the
sweet smell and taste of blackcurrant
itself.

"Oh, wow!" said Felicity, spinning
around with an enormous grin on her
face. "This is incredible! I feel like I'm
inside a blackcurrant!"

Just then a silver panel in the room

slid silently back and from behind it came a bubbly fairy, giggling words of welcome.

"So lovely you could come! How super to see you all!" she trilled. "My name is Bella and I will be your guide today."

Felicity, Holly, Polly and Winnie couldn't say a thing. All their mouths were so busy being wide open in shock that no words would come! Bella looked beautiful... in the weirdest way imaginable!

Bella's hair didn't look like hair. It was an intense pink colour and sculpted on top of her head like the top of an enormous candyfloss. Her dress shimmered and sparkled with such an intensity of colour, each of the fairy friends had to shield her eyes.

"It's been made out of vintage sweet papers," said Bella, noticing their reaction. She spun round so that

the dress flared out, nearly knocking
them over. "And my shoes are made
of real strawberry liquorice," she said,
tiptoeing to give the fairies a better
look.

"Wow!" was all they could say!

✳ ✳ ✳

The tour was tremendous. There were one hundred and two rooms and each was dedicated to a different sweet. Whilst each room looked like the first when they walked in, Bella soon showed them that with one flick of a secret switch the silver panels on all the walls slid silently back to reveal a room full of complicated tubes,

MAGIC
MIXING
VAT

bubbling machines, noisy mixers and a deliciously tempting conveyor belt covered with the finished sweet itself. Busy sweet-making fairies rushed around furiously in clinical white outfits and crowns that tucked their hair up and away from they face. It was amazing to see the entire sweet being made, from the raw ingredients

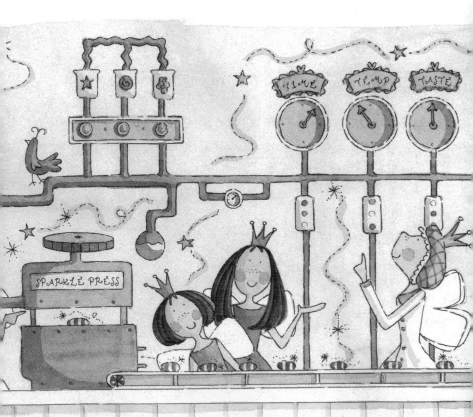

to the final sparkling
wrapped product
they were used
to seeing in
Fairy Mart.

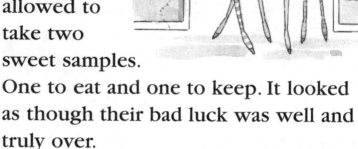

And to the
fairies' delight,
as they left
each room,
they were
allowed to
take two
sweet samples.
One to eat and one to keep. It looked
as though their bad luck was well and
truly over.

* * *

But, by the end of the tour, none of
the fairy friends wanted to see
another sweet ever again! Polly's new
dedication to having fun had persuaded
her, Felicity, Holly and Winnie not only
to eat the one hundred and two sample

sweets they were given to try, but to also eat the ones they were given to keep.

Two hundred and four sweets later, each of the fairies was feeling sicker than they'd explained in the fake sick notes they'd posted to Fairy Godmother.

* * *

On Monday morning, Daisy waited anxiously by the doors to the school assembly hall. It was perfectly normal for Felicity to be late, but it was unlike all her friends to arrive after nine.

By mid-morning break she had tried all their phone numbers, but none of them was answering. What if something had happened to them on the way to the Sweet Factory? She was the only one that knew the truth of where they had been.

Daisy was faced with a difficult decision, but by lunch-time she had made it. She went to Fairy Godmother's office.

"Fairy Godmother," she began tentatively, "I'm a bit worried about Felicity, Polly, Winnie and Holly."

"I bet you are," said Fairy Godmother, kindly putting her arm around the small fairy and ushering her into her office. "But all poorly fairies get better in the end. It's much more important they rest. It would only take them longer to recover if they came to school, and besides, we don't want the whole of Nine Wishes going down with their bug."

Daisy looked awkward and squirmed in her seat.

"I don't think they are sick," she said bravely. "I've got a horrid feeling something has happened to them."

"Whatever makes you think that?" asked Fairy Godmother, concerned. "None of your friends would be out flying if they were sick. I'm sure they're tucked up safely in bed."

Daisy was distraught. She didn't know what to say. She didn't want to expose her friends' lies, but she needed to know they were OK.

"I had a dream," said Daisy, telling a little white lie. "Last night I dreamt that something dreadful had happened to them."

Fairy Godmother sat up. Dreams were very important in Fairy World and were never thought silly. "Then we must go at once," she said.

✳ ✳ ✳

When Daisy and Fairy Godmother reached Felicity's house, they found the door slightly ajar. Tiptoeing in, they found all four fairies tucked up sound asleep in Felicity's bed. A large empty Make it Better medicine bottle stood on the bedside table.

Fairy Godmother was just about to

call the doctor when she noticed
hundreds of sweet wrappers hidden
under the bed!

Felicity rubbed her eyes and sat up.
She didn't look well at all.

"Please excuse us," whispered Fairy
Godmother, trying not to wake the
other fairies. "We had to let ourselves
in. Daisy had a dream that something
dreadful had happened to you!"

Felicity didn't know what to say.
She didn't want to get her friends in

trouble, but she also knew that she couldn't tell a lie, especially to Fairy Godmother.

"Something dreadful did happen," said Felicity slowly.

Daisy winced. Surely Felicity wasn't about to tell Fairy Godmother the truth?

"The truth is," continued Felicity, "that bad luck happens to everyone. Nothing in Fairy World will ever stop that."

Fairy Godmother nodded wisely.

Felicity continued, "And the only thing we can do about it is to stay true to ourselves. Reacting to bad luck in a bad way will only make its magic more powerful and make it worse."

Fairy Godmother smiled knowingly. "It seems as if you've all learnt a very important lesson. I think the best thing now is for Daisy and I to leave you fairies while you rest and concentrate on making yourselves better."

And as Felicity nestled back down under her duvet she made a vow never, ever to eat another sweet!

Well, not until she was feeling much better, anyway!

True fun happens naturally

don't plan it,
just let it happen!

Fairy Fun

The arrival of spring each year in Little Blossoming was marked by a very special day. It was a day when every single fairy in the School of Nine Wishes flew with apprehension until noon. It was Fairy Fool's Day!

* * *

"Oh, goodness," said Felicity, wings quivering, when she met Holly at the corner. "I'm not sure I want to go to school this morning!"

"After last year I don't blame you!" laughed Holly, who remembered how silly Felicity had looked when someone had put sticky feathers on her seat.

"By the way," said Felicity, looking intently at Holly's face, "you've got pen on the end of your nose."

Holly rubbed her nose hard. "Gone?" she asked.

Felicity stared at it. "Nope, still there."

Holly licked the tips of her fingers and rubbed again.

"Gone now?" she asked.

Felicity looked very seriously at

Holly. "I don't think it's ever going to come off," she said, trying to keep a straight face.

Holly went pale. She loved to look perfect at all times. "This is a disaster! What am I going to do? I will never become a Christmas Fairy now, without my looks."

And then she saw Felicity grinning back at her.

"Happy Fairy Fool's Day!" said Felicity, pleased that her first trick of the morning had worked!

* * *

Everything appeared to be pretty normal when the fairies reached the school gates to meet the rest of their friends. Normal, that was, until Polly turned round to lead them all into assembly. On her back someone had stuck a note saying, "Hug me!"

Felicity, Winnie, Holly and Daisy nearly fell over laughing.

"What's so funny?" asked Polly,
spinning round.

"Nothing!" said Felicity, hugging
her friend.

"Nope, not a thing!" said Winnie and
Daisy, hugging Polly at the same time.

"Nothing is funny at all!" said Holly,
giggling hysterically as she squeezed
a hug from her friend.

"Morning, Polly!" said Fairy
Godmother, giving Polly a hug.

"Erm, good morning Fairy Godmother!" said Polly, taken aback. It wasn't like Fairy Godmother to be so informal at school!

* * *

As the school settled down to assembly, Fairy Godmother came on to the stage.

"Welcome, fairies," she began. "I have a very special surprise for you today. We have a wonderful guest speaker who has an amazing talent, and she has kindly offered to share that talent with you at break-time on the tennis courts. But before you decide whether or not you'd like to join her, let me first introduce you to Sophie, the Wingless Flying Fairy!"

Shocked gasps rippled throughout the hall and everyone clapped as Sophie flew on to the stage without the use of wings!

* * *

"That was amazing!" said Felicity to her friends when they left assembly to walk to their first lesson.

"I know," said Holly. "Really incredible. Imagine being able to fly without wings. Think how liberating it would be!"

"Yes," agreed Winnie. "There would be no wings to get caught up in things."

"You couldn't get wing-ache!" observed Polly.

"And there would be no need to get new pairs when the old ones wear out!" said Daisy.

"It would be great!" said Felicity, who was always losing her wings.

So they all agreed that they would go to Sophie's Wingless Flying class together at break-time – with almost every other fairy in the school.

* * *

Felicity was looking forward to her

first lesson, cooking class, because
they were making double-choc cookies.
She was just about to go in
when her mobile phone rang.

"Erm, this is Fairy
Godmother's secretary,"
said the deep voice.
"Could you come and
see her immediately?"

Felicity gulped. Fairy
Godmother's secretary
had never phoned her
before. She hoped she
wasn't in trouble.

"Do you know what
she wants me for?" she
ventured tentatively.

The secretary stumbled
with her reply. "Erm, she
needs your expert advice
on, erm, how to make a triple wand
wish."

"Are you sure?" asked Felicity, who

was terrible at making even the simplest wishes, never mind a triple wand wish.

"Are you questioning Fairy Godmother?" said the gruff secretarial voice.

"Um, no!" said Felicity. "I'll come straight away."

Felicity lost no time in going straight to Fairy Godmother's office. She only had to knock once before Fairy Godmother opened the door.

"Um, hello," said Felicity a little nervously, and without further ado she closed her eyes, desperately tried to remember the words needed to make a triple wand wish, and swung her wand! Suddenly, the whole room was wreathed in fog.

"Felicity! Whatever do you think you're doing?" spluttered Fairy Godmother.

But before Felicity could answer

she saw Holly peeping round the
door, holding her mobile phone and
laughing loudly.

"Oh, Fairy Godmother!" said Felicity
quickly, trying to waft away the fog
with her wand. "I'm very sorry. I think
I've just been the victim of a Fairy
Fool!"

* * *

The rest of the morning was just as
mischievous. In chemistry class,
someone had crawled under the table
and replaced Miss Sparkle's wand

with a banana! In maths, someone
put the clock forward so the class
finished half an hour early. And in PE,
the netballs were filled with helium
so they kept floating off!

* * *

When Felicity, Holly, Polly, Winnie
and Daisy met on the tennis courts at
break-time, they were amazed that
they'd survived intact. There were wet
fairies who'd been caught by delicately
balanced buckets of water on top of

doors; there were fairies with pen-drawn moustaches that they didn't even know they had. There were even fairies whose crowns had secretly been replaced by hats of every description, while they remained completely oblivious!

"I'm just glad this Fairy Fool's day will soon be over!" said Felicity, giving Polly another hug while she could get away with it. "In half an hour any fairy that tries to do a Fairy Fool trick on someone will be a fool herself."

"I don't think there's much opportunity for anyone to pull any surprises now. By the time this class has finished it will all be over for another year," said Polly.

Suddenly, Sophie the Wingless Fairy flew high above the trees and clapped her hands for attention.

"Thank you for attending my extra-special class on learning how to fly without wings," she began. "Before I start this class, I'd like to introduce you to the official photographer for today. So many fairies don't believe you can fly without wings, and want evidence. So, it always helps if I show them photos of previous classes."

A fairy with an enormous camera flew up using her wings to hover next to Sophie. She waved wildly at the crowd below.

"So," continued Sophie, "I'd like to start this class by asking you all to choose a partner."

Each of the fairies on the tennis courts turned to the nearest person to her.

"Lovely," Sophie said when she saw everyone had a partner. "Now, I'd like you to stand back-to-back while I fly amongst you with this special silver thread. One of the most important parts of learning how to fly without wings is knowing what you'd do without them. My aim is to tangle you up so that you lose the control of your wings even though you are wearing them."

It was a strange concept for Felicity and her friends to grapple with, but they could see the logic in it. Finally, when Sophie had managed to construct an intricate web of silver thread all around the fairies, she asked them to close their eyes.

"For this next stage I'd like you all to hum the tune to "Happy Birthday" out loud," Sophie said to the crowd. "I know this might seem strange to some of you, but it's important that your mind is completely clear of all thoughts. Just try to think of humming the tune and the notes, and nothing else. When you feel as though you have reached that point then I'd like you all to cluck like chickens."

Felicity, Polly, Daisy and Winnie tried to stifle their giggles. Holly opened her eyes suspiciously.

"Keep your eyes closed," continued Sophie. "It sounds silly, I know, but chickens can't fly, even though they wish they could. If you can get in touch with your inner chicken then you will be well on the way to flying without wings. I did it, and I know you can too!"

So, without any further instruction from Sophie, more than one hundred students at the School of Nine Wishes

stood back-to-back with a partner,
bound in silver thread, started to hum
"Happy Birthday" and then one by one
practise their best chicken impressions.
All in an attempt to learn how to fly
without wings.

* * *

Felicity, Holly, Polly, Daisy and Winnie
had been clucking quite convincingly
for more than five minutes with their
eyes closed. None of them, or indeed
any of the other hundred clucking
fairies, dared open their eyes or stop
their chicken impressions until they
heard further instruction from Sophie.

As fairies they knew how important it was to follow a magic recipe to the letter in order for it to work. But after ten minutes Holly couldn't keep it going any longer.

"Do you think, CLUCK, that it's OK, CLUCK, to open our eyes?" she said to Felicity.

"I'm not CLUCK, CLUCK, CLUCK, sure," said Felicity.

"Oh, wand sticks!" said Holly. "I don't care about flying without wings. I'm fed up of this. I'm going to open my eyes nowwwwwww…" and Holly's voice trailed off.

"You're never going to believe this!" she said, shouting out as loudly as she could. "EVERYONE! OPEN YOUR EYES! LOOK!"

And as Holly's message spread and one by one each of the fairies opened their eyes, they were greeted by an extraordinary sight.

In the space in the sky where Sophie the Wingless Fairy had been, there was an enormous banner. On it were the words, "Happy Fairy Fool's Day!" and beside it flew the photographer with her enormous camera, taking photos of them all. And as she darted around it was plain to see *The Daily Flutter* newspaper logo on her t-shirt.

Happy Fairy Fool's Day!

There was no escape! All one hundred fairies were trapped together with silver thread. By the next morning, every fairy in the whole of Little Blossoming would know how gullible they'd been.

* * *

Next day's issue of *The Daily Flutter* sold more copies in one day than it had in the entire previous week. The headline read: "Fairies Fooled by Fairy Godmother!"

"It says here that Sophie was a fake!" said Daisy, aghast.

"Of course she was!" said Holly.

"She used a harness and wires when she flew onto the stage in assembly, and when we were outside on the tennis courts she was attached to a line that was held by the trees."

"We were all so anxious to believe she could fly without wings, no one looked for clues to disprove it," said Felicity, who was secretly a little disappointed.

"Fairy Godmother was very clever. By the time any of us realized what she had done, it was past noon and too late to get her back!" said Polly.

"Well, there's always next year!" ventured Felicity – whose mind was already whirring!

fooling friends with fun

makes magical memories
you never forget!

Circus Cheer

Felicity couldn't help thinking that
life in Little Blossoming had become
a little boring over the last few weeks.
Every day seemed the same as the
last, and nothing new had happened
in ages.

But the next day, Felicity flew into
school with news that made every
fairy's wings flap. The fairy circus was
coming to Little Blossoming!

Felicity and her friends Holly, Polly,
Daisy and Winnie had never been to
a circus before. They watched in awe
from the sky as lots of large lorries
arrived in the park.

Fairies of every shape and size imaginable fluttered out and began unpacking huge poles, dragging long ropes and heaving great swathes of material. Bit by bit, they were making tents big enough to fit a whole fairy house inside!

Every day for the next four days Felicity and her friends stopped off at the park on their way to school – and each day less and less of the park remained recognizable.

Finally, on Friday morning, it looked as though it was almost finished in time for the opening night.

None of the fairies at the School of Nine Wishes could contain their excitement. Everyone was finding it hard to concentrate on the last lesson of the day.

As soon as the final bell rang, Felicity, Holly, Polly, Daisy and Winnie flew their fastest to be the first at the park gate. Clutching their tickets carefully, they looked up in awe at the circus lights blazing in the early evening sky. It was magical.

The biggest tent Felicity and her friends had ever seen stood in the centre of the park. Pink-and-white striped canvas fell to the ground from a tall peaked roof, and an enormous neon flashing sign beamed "Big Top!" from its entrance.

All around it stood countless

smaller tents in ice-cream colours, lit up with rows of twinkling fairy lights. Candyfloss stands, coconut shies, merry-go-rounds and fairground rides nestled in between.

Felicity and her fairy friends didn't know where to look first, so they just ran as fast as they could, eager to discover absolutely everything.

"Over here!" shouted Felicity as she hovered above the crowds of excited fairies to point her friends in the direction of the hoopla stand. "You can win an inflatable wand!"

"But look over here!" said Polly, tugging at Holly's arm. "Oh, my goodness!" said her friend with a gulp. "She's TALL!"

"She's not tall, silly!" said Daisy, staring at the fairy walking towards them handing out leaflets. "She's on stilts!"

Felicity fluttered up to catch the leaflet.

★ WANTED ★
Talented and fun fairies required to join the circus! Make every day as exciting as your experience tonight! Applications to Ms Swing-Spangle

Felicity glanced over it, folded the paper and then popped it absent-mindedly into her pocket.

"Come on!" said Holly, noticing the

queue snaking from the door of the Big Top. "We can discover all this after the show. Let's make sure we get a good seat. I want to be near the front!"

Inside the tent was a huge ring with sand on its floor. All the way around it arced low benches, twelve rows deep.

By the time the fairies had waited their turn to give their tickets to the beaming clown fairy at the door, the front row was almost taken up. But the fairy friends were just in time. With a squeeze they just managed to fit on the end of the very last bench.

"Oh, I can't wait!!" breathed Felicity, feeling the electricity in the air.

"It's overwhelming!" said Winnie, as she looked up at the complicated tangle of ropes and pulleys hanging from the ceiling.

"I'm not sure what to expect!" said

Polly, who had read plenty of books from the library on circuses. "Different circuses have different themes. Some have performers doing amazing gymnastic feats, and others have fairies from parts of Fairy World you wouldn't know existed. I saw a picture in one book of a fairy with ten sets of wings!"

"Shhhhhh!" whispered Daisy as the lights dimmed and a bright spotlight made a luminous circle in the middle of the ring. "It's about to begin."

As soon as the fairy ringmaster walked into the spotlight, the audience put down their monkey nuts, stopped eating their candyfloss and rose to their feet to cheer and clap.

"Welcome!" called the ringmaster in a commanding voice. "Welcome to the greatest fairy circus in Fairy World!" The whole tent cheered. "Tonight we have a show that will

entertain you! Delight you! Thrill you!
And fill you with fun! Are you ready
to see the first act?"

"Yesssssss!" shouted Felicity, Holly,
Polly, Daisy and Winnie with the
crowd.

"Well then, without further delay
let me introduce you to... the

MARVELLOUS MAGICAL MINGLING TWINS!"

Suddenly the tent went black. As the clapping gradually subsided, a tiny patch of intense pink light shone from the uppermost point in the tent's ceiling.

"What's that?" whispered Felicity to Polly.

"I don't know," Polly said quietly back. "It looks like a bird... or maybe not..."

All the fairies squinted into the darkness. Very gradually, moment by moment, the light got closer and closer.

"It's twisting..." said Holly in awe. "It's turning... it's not a bird, it's a flame!"

"It's not... it's a fairy!" said Felicity, suddenly seeing the flash of a wing.

"How can she move that fast?" said Polly. She was amazed: the twisting, turning light above their heads seemed to be generated by the speed of the fairy's spinning.

"Oh, my goodness!" burst out Holly, putting her hands over her mouth. "There are two of them. It's two fairies twisting together, at the speed of light!"

As the Marvellous Magical Mingling Twins arrived at eye level, the awestruck fairies took a sharp intake of breath. The twins hovered in mid-air, moving in a way that none of the fairy friends had ever seen before. They couldn't even imagine how they were achieving it. It was as if they were performing an intricate dance so fast that the movements were blurred and all that could be seen was a halo of bright light.

Then, without warning, it stopped. The watching crowd was plunged dramatically into darkness. As the

lights slowly
went up they
revealed the
twins standing
proudly with
arms outstretched.
The audience
in the Big Top
exploded into
rapturous
applause. It
was the most
mind-blowing
thing any of
them had
ever seen.
The
Marvellous
Magical
Mingling
Twins turned
out to be
only the first

in a show full of events that defied the limits of what a normal fairy could achieve.

There was wand-throwing, where a fearless fairy spun around on a wheel while a blindfolded fairy threw pointed starred wands with unbelievable precision. There was a hysterical duo of tiny clown fairies who fell over and covered everyone in the front row with a large bucketful of red paint... which, to Holly's relief,

turned out only to be confetti! And a tightrope-walking fairy who balanced without wings on a thread so thin it couldn't be seen.

When the fairy friends left the Big Top they couldn't stop talking! Each of them had a favourite part of the show and every single one of them was filled with a passion to become part of the circus too.

"What an incredible life it must be!" said Felicity, as they flew slowly home.

"Just imagine learning those skills!" exclaimed Polly.

"Wearing those sparkling sequinned outfits!" breathed Holly.

"Having all that excitement every night!" said Winnie.

"Let's go back tomorrow!" said Daisy. "I really want to meet the clowns. They made me laugh so much!"

The fairy friends didn't just return to the circus the next night, they went the night after that and the night after that too. In fact, they went every night for the whole week. And if it hadn't been for school they would have gone in the day as well.

Each night they discovered new and exciting things and made friends with more circus performers.

After the most spectacular night yet, Felicity and her friends peeked into the private tent belonging to the Marvellous Magical

Mingling Twins. They were desperate to meet the stars of the show.

Holly, being a rather impatient fairy, gave Felicity a gentle push forwards into the tent. The twins turned round just as Felicity came flying through the door.

"Sorry, I don't want to disturb you after your amazing performance," said Felicity, feeling her cheeks go pink, "but we just wanted to tell you how much we admire your work!"

One of the twins helped Felicity off the ground. "I'm Molly, and this is my sister Miranda," she said, smiling. "We're so glad you enjoyed the show. Would you and your friends like to come in?"

The fairies didn't need asking twice. They spent the most wonderful evening trying on the twins' sparkling costumes and fabulous make-up, and hearing all about life on the road.

By the end of the evening they were the best of friends.

But the circus was only staying for a week. On the day it moved on, Felicity and her friends raced down to the park after school more quickly than they had ever flown before, to see their new friends off. But as they rounded the corner, their hearts sank as they saw the last truck pulling out of the park and leaving Little Blossoming for ever.

Felicity, Holly, Polly, Daisy and Winnie stood sadly in the empty field.

"Our new friends have gone!" cried Felicity, tears in her eyes.

"What will we do without them?" said Daisy, watching a leftover balloon float gently into the sky.

"Things won't be half as much fun now they've gone," said Holly.

Felicity wanted to be a Friendship Fairy when she graduated from the School of Nine Wishes. She always made friends for life and she couldn't think of anything worse than losing her new best friends.

"Maybe we don't have to do without them!" said Felicity, putting her hand deep into her coat pocket and pulling out the leaflet she'd been handed on the first day the circus had come to town.

"What do you mean?" asked Holly.

"I mean," said Felicity, opening it out

to show them, "why don't we join the circus!"

"Don't be silly!" said Polly. "We can't just leave our homes and our friends behind."

"But what about our new friends?" Felicity was determined. "Let's at least go after them and talk to them about it!"

"What are we waiting for?" said Winnie, her wings quivering with adventure. "Their tyre tracks are leading in the direction of Bloomfield. If we fly across the fields, we'll be able to catch them up before they get there."

So, without another moment's thought, the five fairy friends leapt into the air. This was it! This was where their new exciting life was to begin: no more school, no more homework, no more boring Little Blossoming. From now on, fairy life was going to be all fun. Clowning around in the morning, daring dinner-times and exciting evenings… not to mention non-stop candyfloss treats and fairground rides!

"Oh, look!" said Felicity, bubbling over with excitement. "I can see them! We've almost caught them up!" She pointed towards nine trucks waiting by the side of the road.

"They've broken down!" said Holly. "Quick, let's go and help!"

The circus convoy had stopped to mend a tyre on one of the trucks. But before they could get to it, Felicity and her friends were distracted by angry voices. The Marvellous Magical Mingling Twins seemed to be having the most enormous argument.

"What's wrong?" asked Felicity, landing beside them with a fairylike thud. "Please don't argue. I'm sure you can work things out. Can we help?"

"It's just that I'm fed up!" said Miranda. "Molly thinks the circus is fun, but I think it's really hard work!"

"I have NEVER called it fun!" Molly said firmly. "It's a hard life in the circus. We're always on the road. The moment we make new friends and settle, we're off to somewhere new and have to say goodbye."

Molly and Miranda looked pale and washed out without their bright costumes and make-up. Felicity also noticed blisters on their hands and feet from all their rope acrobatics.

"What I'd really love is to be at the School of Nine Wishes with you and lead a normal life," admitted Miranda to Felicity.

Felicity, Holly, Polly, Daisy and Winnie couldn't believe their ears.

"Well, just go!" said Molly crossly. "Leave me to do the act alone. I can change the name to the Marvellous

Magical Mingling Molly."

Miranda calmed down. "You know I would never leave the circus. It's my life. I was made to be part of it. But it's hard sometimes."

"Sometimes leading a 'normal' life is difficult too," said Felicity. "We don't always have the fun you imagine. But we do have our friends and our homes in Little Blossoming. And you have yours in the circus."

Miranda nodded. "You're right. Every time we have to leave new friends, it's a struggle. But we know in our hearts that we belong here, in the circus. And we are looking forward to tonight's performance in Bloomfield."

Felicity and her friends all gave Miranda and Molly big goodbye hugs, swapped addresses so they could become pen pals, and promised to meet up when the circus was back in town.

"Our hearts belong in Little Blossoming," said Felicity, "just like yours belong to the circus!"

fun is in your heart

carry it with you,
wherever you go!

Emma Thomson's

Felicity Wishes®

Felicity and her friends

find a magical place

to have a picnic in

Clutter Clean-out

River Rescue

With jammy fingers, Felicity Wishes brushed her hair out of her eyes.

"It's hard work making picnics!" said Felicity to her friend Polly.

"But fun!" said Polly, taking a damp cloth and wiping the jam off Felicity's nose.

It was Saturday; no fairy school! Felicity and her three fairy friends Holly, Daisy and Polly had decided to go on a picnic. Holly had volunteered to bring the rug, cups and plates, Daisy was in charge of bringing something yummy to drink, and Polly and Felicity were making the sandwiches and snacks.

"I think I'm nearly done!" said Felicity, standing back and admiring her jam sandwich mountain.

"My cheesy puffs will be ready soon," said Polly, looking at the clock on the cooker. "We've just got time to fly to the apple tree and pick some fruit, and our picnic will be complete!" The fairies raced each other to the orchard at the bottom of the garden.

* * *

When they turned up at Holly's house they thought she had forgotten all about their plans.

"Sorry to keep you waiting," said Holly when she eventually opened her front door. "I was having a colour coordinating dilemma."

Felicity and Polly raised their eyebrows.

"I just can't decide between the green checked rug and the yellow daisy-design plates, or the pink rose rug and the blue spotty plates," she explained. "Come and see!"

The fairy friends followed Holly through the house and out into her back garden. They were used to Holly having this sort of dramatic dilemma.

"There's no choice!" said Felicity, looking down at both sets laid out side by side.

"It has to be the pink rose rug. When in doubt, choose pink!" she said, because pink was her favourite colour.

* * *

With heavy bags weighing them down, Holly, Polly and Felicity reached Daisy's house. She was already waiting outside on her front steps.

"Where shall we go?" said Daisy, flying up to meet them.

"I don't know, let's flutter around for a bit until we see somewhere nice," suggested Polly.

"I'm not flying too far with this heavy bag!" said Holly. "Let's go up really high so we can see the whole of Little Blossoming and Bloomfield and choose from there."

"Yeah!" they all agreed excitedly.

It was Polly who spotted a place they'd never been before.

"Look!" she said. "Down there," and she pointed to a twinkly blue thread of water winding in and out of the dip of the hills.

"It looks like a magical river," said Felicity, dreamily. "You can see it glisten as the sunlight catches its surface."

* * *

The river was just as wonderful as it had looked from the sky. On either side of its banks tall plants gave shade to tiny schools of fish. Lily pads broke the surface with heavy flowers in pinks and whites, and a small waterfall at the top made a sound that was delicious enough to make you want to drink.

"This is bliss!" said Felicity, lying back in her pink dress on the pink rose rug, munching happily on a raspberry jam sandwich.

"It's beautiful!' said Holly, who was down at the water's edge, gazing at her reflection.

"Just lovely!" agreed Polly, who had already thrown off her tights and shoes and was sploshing her feet in the water.

"It's also incredibly interesting!" said Daisy. She wanted to be a Blossom Fairy one day, and had brought along her flower book so that she could identify anything she might not recognize.

"Look at this lily pad," she called, pointing. "It's so magical it moves all by itself."

Felicity knelt down beside her. "You're right! It is moving all by itself!"

"Let me see!" said Polly, jumping up with a start. As she swung her feet out of the water with a huge splosh, the lily pad jumped up in the air!

"Aghh!" squealed Daisy, as she lost her balance and fell into the water.

"I'll save you!" said Felicity, throwing off her shoes.

"It's not deep, just wet!" said Daisy, laughing as she stood up, knee deep.

"Look!" said Holly, springing to her feet and pointing with a squeal. "It's not a magical lily pad – it's a frog!"

All the fairy friends watched in awe as a little green frog hopped from one large leaf to another.

"I've never seen a frog in real life before," said Felicity.

"I don't expect he's ever seen a fairy!" said Holly.

"I wonder," mused Felicity, as she helped Daisy out of the water, "if he'd like to make friends."

With Daisy safely on dry land, Felicity set about making her acquaintance with the little green frog.

* * *

By the end of the afternoon the little frog and Felicity were inseparable.

"I don't want it to be time to go home already," said Felicity, glumly. "It's been the most perfect day. I couldn't eat another jam sandwich if I tried."

"We can always come another day, now we've found this magical spot," said Polly, practically.

"Let's make it our secret picnic place!" said Holly.

"I need to come back and finish my

notes," said Daisy, putting the lid back on her pen. "There are so many flowers here that I've never seen before."

"I don't want it to be too long before I see my new frog friend again," said Felicity. "Let's make a promise to come back here soon." And all the fairy friends agreed.

Read the rest of

Emma Thomson's

felicity Wishes®

Clutter Clean-out

to discover what happens

to the fairies' secret place.

If you enjoyed this book, why not try
another of these fantastic story collections?

Designer Drama

Star Surprise

Clutter Clean-out

Newspaper Nerves

Enchanted Escape

Whispering Wishes

7 Sensational Secrets

8 Friends Forever

9 Happy Hobbies

10 Party Pickle

11 Wand Wishes

12 Dancing Dreams

14 Fashion Fiasco

13 Spooky Sleepover

15 Pink Paradise

17 Dreamy Daisy

16 Spectacular Skies

18 Perfect Polly

Holly's Hideaway

Winnie's Wonderland

Fairy Fun

Look out for these three special editions

Summer Sunshine

Christmas Calamity

Winter Wishes

See Your Friendship Letter Here!

Write in and tell us all about your best friend, and you could see your letter published in one of the Felicity Wishes books.

Please send in your letter, including your name and age, with a stamped self-addressed envelope to:

Felicity Wishes Friendship Competition

Hodder Children's Books, 338 Euston Road, London NW1 3BH

Australian readers should write to...
Hachette Children's Books
Level 17/207 Kent Street, Sydney, NSW 2000, Australia

New Zealand readers should write to...
Hachette Children's Books
PO Box 100-749 North Shore Mail Centre, Auckland, New Zealand

Closing date is 30 April 2007

ALL ENTRIES MUST BE SIGNED BY A PARENT OR GUARDIAN.
TO BE ELIGIBLE ENTRANTS MUST BE UNDER 13 YEARS.

For full terms and conditions visit www.felicitywishes.net/terms

Friends of Felicity

Dear Felicity

My best friend is called Emily. She is fun to play with and we love having sleepovers together. I trust her not to tell tell anyone my secrets. She has a good sense of humour and always makes me giggle and we always go in partners at school. I no we will stay friends for ever and ever

lots g love Hannah x x x x x x
age 10

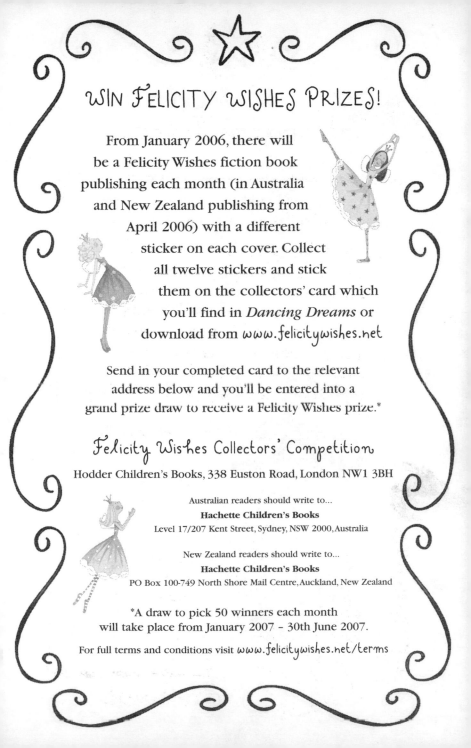

WIN FELICITY WISHES PRIZES!

From January 2006, there will
be a Felicity Wishes fiction book
publishing each month (in Australia
and New Zealand publishing from
April 2006) with a different
sticker on each cover. Collect
all twelve stickers and stick
them on the collectors' card which
you'll find in *Dancing Dreams* or
download from www.felicitywishes.net

Send in your completed card to the relevant
address below and you'll be entered into a
grand prize draw to receive a Felicity Wishes prize.*

Felicity Wishes Collectors' Competition

Hodder Children's Books, 338 Euston Road, London NW1 3BH

Australian readers should write to...
Hachette Children's Books
Level 17/207 Kent Street, Sydney, NSW 2000, Australia

New Zealand readers should write to...
Hachette Children's Books
PO Box 100-749 North Shore Mail Centre, Auckland, New Zealand

*A draw to pick 50 winners each month
will take place from January 2007 – 30th June 2007.

For full terms and conditions visit www.felicitywishes.net/terms

WOULD YOU LIKE TO BE A FRIEND OF FELICITY?

Felicity Wishes has her very own website, filled with lots of sparkly fairy fun and information about Felicity Wishes and all her fairy friends.

Just visit:

www.felicitywishes.net

to find out all about Felicity's books, sign up to competitions, quizzes and special offers.

And if you want to show how much you love your friends, you can even send them a Felicity e-card for free. It will truly brighten up their day!

For full terms and conditions visit www.felicitywishes.net/terms